Spell Songs is a musical companion piece to

THE LOST WORDS

by Robert Macfarlane and Jackie Morris © 2017

Published by Hamish Hamilton, an imprint of Penguin Books

spell songs

FOLK BY THE OAK

FOR SIMON PROSSER:

We gave you an acorn.
You planted it.
A forest grew.

Robert Macfarlane
and Jackie Morris

CREATING SPELL SONGS

Astounded by Jackie Morris and Robert Macfarlane's remarkable book *The Lost Words: A Spell Book*, I eagerly listened to their enlightening conversation at Hay Winter Festival 2017. On the overhead screen they played a video of composer Kerry Andrew's musical response to *Wren* spell. A few fluttering, textural, clustered consonants and haunting vocals later and the musicality of the spells shone out at me. Our festival, Folk by the Oak, has been lucky enough to have created three previous musical collaborations and with this in mind I arrived back home, read the *Otter* spell to Adam, and in an instant we both knew *Spell Songs* had to be!

With the full support of avid folk music fans Robert and Jackie, and with the discerning advice and support of Neil Pearson our project manager, we proceeded to calm our excitement and think seriously about gathering in musicians. A love of nature, a concern for conservation, tonal quality, innate talent, cultural influences, delicious speaking and singing voices, a love of books, an understanding of the collaborative process, true professionalism and an experience of many musical genres all came into the mix when we put forward each musician. Fate was also at work: we soon discovered that a few of our proposed musicians had independently contacted Rob and Jackie already curious to know if they could bring music to *The Lost Words*.

At this stage all we had was an instinctive, intuitive 'feel' for how they would sound together. We had no idea what the outcome would be and we deliberately stepped well back from any creative decisions from this point onwards.

Then followed a blustery September gathering at Greta Hall in Keswick, once home to Samuel Taylor Coleridge. There was a memorable walk up Cat Bells led by Robert, an afternoon in conversation about *The Lost Words* book whilst watching Jackie conjure ink-brushed otters and an evening of music making. In early January came the start of the residency proper — four days at Monnington House in Herefordshire followed by four days recording at Rockfield Studio in Monmouthshire. Forward to the February sell-out tour culminating at

The Southbank Centre's Queen Elizabeth Hall in London, and *Spell Songs* had indeed become something very special, exceeding all expectations.

And wonderful discoveries were made; the creative connection between Kris and Seckou, the breath-taking affinity between Karine and Julie's voices, the warm appreciation of the power and beauty of Beth and Jim's voices, the realisation of how deeply harpist Rachel cared for the songs and their makers (with a tear or two on stage), hearing Karine's heartfelt motivating words on conservation and, of course, the beautiful bond between fine artist and musicians which grew and grew.

And who would have imagined that birds would alight gently upon the musicians and choose them as their human embodiment? Jackie's new paintings, created solely for this CD book, blur the world of music, humanity and nature; an artistic, sound-filled, species-hopping synaesthesia. They are a true delight to behold.

Each song that has been created comes from the heart – from the heart of a rare and special book and from the heart of a true collaboration with a wealth of music-making experience at its core; where creativity was an open and instinctive act and where generosity of musicianship became a true gift to all.

Thank you, Spell Singers – you have moved us and motivated us in an age where the natural world hangs in the balance. Like the golden one in flight, you've left your little gifts of light . . .

Thank you, Robert and Jackie – for creating something as powerful as *The Lost Words*.

Thank you, Adam Slough and Neil Pearson – for believing in my idea and making it happen.

Caroline Slough
Folk by the Oak Festival Director

Spell Songs grew out of *The Lost Words* by Robert Macfarlane and Jackie Morris. If *The Lost Words* became a forest, then *Spell Songs* is the birds in the trees. Together they deepen the experience of looking at and listening to the wild; each a companion to the other.

ROBERT MACFARLANE

Two memories from the making of this music. The first – a September dawn in the Lake District. Dishwater-grey skies. Rain drifting across the hills. Scant promise of a break in the weather. Still, we all set off – musicians, artists, writers, producers – and walked together, into a headwind, up Cat Bells above Derwent Water. And as we neared the top, people helping each other up the steeper parts, an everyday miracle occurred. The clouds tore open, sun blazed through the gap and we stood as a group on the summit, watching light glitter on the lake's surface and the wet rock of the fells. To the landscape, it was nothing but business as usual. To us, it felt like a blessing.

The second, six months later. A January morning in Cambridge. My inner weather had been overcast for almost a month; greyer than I'd ever known it before. Not much sign of it clearing, either. Then I listened to the first bars I'd heard of the music of *Spell Songs*: studio roughs of the 'Lark' song, with Jim Molyneux and Kris Drever's voices lifting and deepening the words into something strange and new. I felt shivers pass through my whole body, scalp to toe; good shivers, the kind that shake you clean and clear. It was the beginning of the end of the clouds. The song called the sun back.

It took Jackie Morris and me two years – from 2015 to 2017 – to make *The Lost Words*. The book's form was very simple. We took twenty common names for twenty common species of plant and creature, forming a crooked almost-A-to-Z from "acorn" to "wren" by way of "conker", "kingfisher", "otter", "willow" and others. For each of these "lost words" – "lost" in the sense that they are slipping from our stories, minds, dictionaries and habitats – I wrote a spell-poem, designed to be spoken or sung aloud in an act of summoning back. And Jackie (who is definitely a magician) conjured each subject onto the page in watercolour and gold leaf; first as absence, then as icon, then fully restored to the habitat of which it is a part. We imagined *The Lost Words* as nothing more or less than what Jackie has called "a beautiful protest" against the loss of everyday nature from our everyday lives in Britain and beyond.

We did not know it then, of course, but *The Lost Words* was itself to become a wild creature, given unpredictable life by the energy and imagination of individuals and communities. Grass-roots campaigns have so far raised money to place copies of the book in every primary and special school in all of Scotland, half of England and a quarter of Wales; similar campaigns are now spreading to North America. The book is used by charities and carers working with dementia-sufferers, with refugees, with survivors of domestic abuse, with childhood cancer patients, and with people in terminal care (those who have lost words in other senses). The book's images and words have been adapted for dance, outdoor theatre, classical and choral music, and turned into tens of thousands of primary school projects, producing a wave of creativity just at a time when funding for music and art is being cut in schools. A copy of the book is now in every hospice in the country, and the new Royal National Orthopaedic Hospital at Stanmore has four levels decorated floor to ceiling with Jackie's art and the spells – a book become a building.

I have come to think of *The Lost Words* as a wildwood that has grown impossibly from an acorn – but it might also be imagined as a selkie of a book, that slips its skin and changes its matter as different people respond to it. Undoubtedly one of its most thrilling transformations has been into the music that you hold in your hand, and I suspect will soon hold in your heart, brought about by the vision and brilliance of eight musicians, who have together taken *The Lost Words* and turned it into something diverse, hopeful, moving and new. To me, as to Jackie, listening to them create this music – and seeing them perform it – has been a privilege beyond easy expression. There are songs here that would live with me for the rest of my years, even if I'd had no part in their making.

It's clear to me that the intensity of response to both *The Lost Words* and *Spell Songs* is about far greater forces and feelings than 'just' a book or a performance. We are presently living through an age of loss, for which we are only just starting to find a language of grief. Extinction and extirpation are underway at frightening speed in landscapes both distant and on our doorsteps. What Michael McCarthy has chillingly called 'The Great Thinning' is accelerating. Disappearance – of language, species, loved places, loved people – is the tune of our times. I keep thinking of and quoting Bertolt Brecht's lines from the late 1930s:

> *"In the dark times*
> *Will there also be singing?*
> *Yes, there will also be singing*
> *About the dark times."*

Brecht had it right. What is there to do in the face of loss but to fight for what is beautiful and what is ethical – and to sing your heart out at all dark matter?

JACKIE MORRIS

If *The Lost Words* was created from a frustration and inability to comprehend how we, as a species have moved so far towards perceiving ourselves as somehow outside of the natural world, born of an anger at how we could stand by and watch this happen, then it grew into something more. Nowhere did this absence, this 'othering' of all things wild, reveal itself more clearly than in the falling away of knowledge and naming of the wildlife that surrounds us. Simple, everyday wildlife.

In classroom after classroom children were unable to recognise and name the dandelion – flower of city, suburb, country, gone from the minds and the memories of children. There was no knowledge that a wren was a bird, what a kingfisher was, or heron. It wasn't their fault, but ours. In one class, named Acorn class, someone had forgotten to tell the children what an acorn actually is – the sleeping seed of a tree, a forest in waiting. The book was created as a hope, to re-engage an interest, to refocus the mind's eye, to celebrate the nearby wild and awaken a sense of wonder and awe for this amazing planet we live on.

As artists our main function should be a responsibility to awe.

Much of the subject matter in the book, the reference material, I found so close to my home. I allowed brambles to grow in my garden until my cottage became like something from a fairytale, surrounded by briars. And those briars became a refuge for wrens, sparrows, blackbirds, with blossoms for bees and fruit in the autumn to feed the birds. Ravens flew over my studio, the beat of the air in their wings became a soundtrack to my painting, as did the yak and snicker of bickering magpies building a nest in the blackthorn outside the window. And wren song, and goldfinch chatter, and the music of humans too.

Ideas for images are often found whilst walking, emptying the mind, allowing things in, with the wild soundtrack of wind, bird, raven, buzzard, peregrine keeping me company. Crafting the idea onto paper takes long hours of patience, and that is when I sought the company of musicians. The making of art for me is all about asking and answering questions. It takes concentration, time, thought. It's not always or often a peaceful process. Self-doubt is never far away, but I am learning to make a friend of this creature. You need courage, a willingness to make mistakes. The only way to make art is to do it, be open to the probability of failure, the almost certainty that you will make mistakes. Only by doing it can you learn how to. And only by doing and making will you get better, better to make different mistakes, find new answers.

There was magic around in the working of the book, from my small dog bringing me a raven's feather as I walked, searching for the idea of how to paint an absence of ravens, to the speaking of spells seeming to summon otters where there never before had been otters seen! Not the least of this was that shortly after publication, as the book took root and began a wild and extraordinary life of its own, Robert and I found ourselves working with musicians who had been the soundtrack of our working lives.

Spell Songs gives wings to the book – words and images weave a spell, music created around both word and image carries that spell deeper into the soul.

Very early in the *Spell Songs* project I looked for ways to connect the music, the book and the wild. I wanted to create a series of images that would be portraits of the musicians. Meeting up in the Lake District we talked about the book, how it came to be. Each of the musicians read from the pages, and later played and sang into the evening. I loved seeing the instruments come to life in their hands. Even sitting silent, waiting, you can almost hear the instruments hum. So, taking photos of each, guitar, cello, whistles, drum, kora, I began to sketch them with a bird, thinking not that the musicians should each have a 'spirit animal', but rather the musicians would become the 'spirit human' for each bird.

The first to fall into place was Kris Drever. Silence fell around the table as he read *Raven*. And there is something of the raven about the man, a quiet presence, fierce focus on the moment, a reserve and a sense of mischief and wildness. We spoke of his guitar, a Collings, how it is so beautifully made, crafted, how it held a note, and carried a volume like no other guitar he owned.

Seckou was always an osprey, because he migrates from Senegal to Britain and back, because he worked with Catrin Finch on *SOAR*, a musical suite on the flight of these beautiful birds. He told me how he is the 71st generation of his family to play the kora. Imagine that. So much learning. With 22 strings of the kora to draw the bird soon became tangled in them. Then I used the wrong gold on the piece in places, a howling mistake. I decided to rework the whole piece, then caught sight of it in evening light and realised that the mistakes made it stronger.

When I met Kerry for the first time, the day of the launch of the book, her hair was kingfisher bright, such a spark of creativity. I painted her as a kingfisher rising, from an empty music stand. She's not been well, wasn't with us for much of that first shaping, so the painting was a hope and a spell for her to be well, to rise, sing and set the stream of music alive with burn and glitter.

Karine is a fierce singer, bright, bold, brave. A line from an early song of hers, *"and I can think of better things for hands to make and hearts to sing"* has been part of the mantra of my working life. And her tenor guitar is a beautiful thing, so she perches on its curve as a bright-eyed wren.

Jim sat quietly at first, watching, listening. He plays so many instruments, and first I tried him with a piano, but all the other musicians had been painted

with their own instruments, so I tried again, this time with his drum, stuck with dark tape, and always as a lark rising. When Jim first sang *Little Astronaut* I think everyone forgot to breathe. His voice catches the vulnerability of what it is to be human. And who among us hasn't known our own dark times?

Rachel has such an elegance about her. A woman of laughter and mischief and courage, she broke the silence with the first notes of *Acorn*, wrapped around a tune from Kris. I painted her as an elegant egret perched on her harp. This painting was made during the residency at Monnington House in Herefordshire, working away with the door open and the sound of the music shaping and building down below. Others were sketched while listening to the music – image and music taking shape together.

Beth became a charm of finches as she drew out the goldfinch song. Her cello is such a thing of beauty. It looks as if it is alive and indeed when she draws the bow across it seems to breathe. At first a single finch sat perched on the scroll, but then others flew into the painting.

Julie was the hardest. She sings of the white hare, the selkie, but I wanted to keep the theme of the birds. I sketched a curlew, but that was the wrong colour, too heavy. Then a flock of lapwings danced into view. Pale skin, dark hair, fine featured, light. It seemed so obvious. So a lapwing spreads wide its wings over the pipes and whistles as she plays. A curracag in Gaelic, fierce in its defence of the young.

And so *Spell Songs* takes flight. Our wish is that it will help to focus anew on all that is precious. We are not 'stewards' of the natural world, we are not something that stands apart from it. We are a very small part of an amazing ecosystem. The Earth is our home, but it is also home to so many forms of life, life that is so astonishing, intelligence that puts our arrogance to shame. We need to find better ways to live, ways that give respect to all life. Our desire is that *Spell Songs* will be a harbour for the soul, a chorus of hope in the dark days, a rallying cry. These are songs of protest, of praise, and of blessing. May they lift your hearts and give you hope.

kerry andrew

Musician, composer, songwriter, multi-instrumentalist and author

---

*An astonishingly perceptive musician,
whose Wren Song composition inspired us to
pursue the idea of a musical companion piece to
The Lost Words. Her love of nature and folklore
combined with her innate musicality are key
reasons why we are delighted that she
accepted our invitation to join Spell Songs.*

KERRY ANDREW

I met Rob via Twitter, having thanked him for his inclusion of the riverine old Northern English word keld in his book *Landmarks* – I'd been scratching around for a title for my freshwater folklore-inspired *You Are Wolf* album. This led to him listening to my bird-populated first album, and especially a song called *Little Wren*, a reinvention of a 12th-century traditional song.

In the summer of 2017, Rob sent me an email asking if I might fancy reading or perhaps doing something musical with a small text he'd written for an upcoming book. Attached were his words for his acrostic spell *Wren*, along with sumptuous artwork by Jackie Morris. Ever-keen to make creative buddies – and because his words were so naturally musical – I whipped up a short a cappella piece setting his spell, including spoken word, extra-vocal techniques and loads of looping, as is my wont.

Happily, it went down well. The book came out to glorious acclaim, and I met both Rob and Jackie for the first time at an event at Foyles in London. Jackie seemed taken with my then-blue hair and called me a kingfisher. The two later asked me to do another spell for an event at the Foundling Museum, where Jackie's shimmering illustrations were being displayed. This time, I set *Bluebell*, picking up my flute for the first time in about 12 years, and adding a ringing wine glass and some bells alongside my layered vocals. I made the song at my desk, the words in front of me, turning the page occasionally to let the indigo-violet wash of colour infuse the song.

I was stoked to be asked to be part of this larger project alongside awe-inspiring (and fangirl-making) musicians. And therefore desperately sad not to be able to be at the writing residency in full force, due to illness. Everyone has been so super-kind in including me where they could, and I thank them with full heart for their generosity.

Singer, songwriter and guitarist

Kris Drever is one of Scotland's finest and most prolific songwriters. He is a fiercely talented guitarist; rated among folk's best, and a singer whose voice is rich with both clarity and resonance. A key collaborator within the multi-award winning trio Lau and a sought after solo artist, Kris' presence in Spell Songs is highly valued and gladly welcomed.

KRIS DREVER

The first raven I saw was a huge solitary ball of night time at the Grind o' Da Navir. I had assumed I'd previously seen them, in Orkney or in Scotland. I knew as soon as I did though, that I had been mistaken.

Eshaness is a long way from anywhere, even in Shetlandic terms. It's a place where sea giants throw huge rocks onto the land, sometimes up 40ft banks.

It looked so at ease at the top, at home, taking care of business. I was barely even a curiosity to it.

So focussed, waiting and watching, it registered me for two or three withering seconds, then headed off down the cliff to its next appointment. It left me with such a strong impression of self-possession that I can recall exactly its gaze now and at any time I choose, years later.

That's a state I covet, a place I've known intimately and distantly and mostly occasionally. The place where everything is thinnest. It is where, if you can find it, special things can happen through ordinary actions; you move as if guided.

The *Spell Songs* asked us to deliver an album's worth of new music, to write it in four days and to record it in three (or maybe the other way round?). In the end, although we didn't get everything recorded, we wrote twenty brand new pieces. We had to make a conscious group decision to stop creating.

I can't speak for everyone but as soon as Rachel kicked the ball and rhythmic discussion began with Seckou, the moment Jim started to hunt for a way through the *Lark* to C#m and as soon as we all sang together like bairns, everything peripheral faded away.

When you get involved in things that play out like this one, the moments of creation always whizz past. You're left with the residue of the process in the form of music and songs but little of what guided you to make the decisions you made. It's why we keep having to go back and make more things. It's the doing that keeps it real, the act of creating. The focus that belongs so completely to animals and birds. It's beautiful and weird.

Julie Fowlis

Singer, songwriter and multi-instrumentalist, voiceover
artist and TV/radio presenter. Scotland's inaugural
Gaelic Ambassador and prolific multilingual collaborator

*Julie Fowlis often sings in Scottish Gaelic and is
deeply influenced by her early upbringing in the Outer
Hebridean island of North Uist. Her crystalline and
intoxicating voice fills this project with genuine beauty
and her Gaelic heritage brings another layer of language
and experience into the Spell Songs ensemble.*

JULIE FOWLIS

I first heard mention of Robert Macfarlane whilst talking to my great friend and one of the foremost singers of Gaelic song, Mary Smith, whilst discussing an amazing document called *Some Lewis Moorland Terms: A Peat Glossary*. After that, when I spotted Robert's book *The Gifts of Reading* in a bookshop in Glasgow, I immediately bought it, followed by *Landmarks*, in which the glossary of peat words featured. As a Gaelic speaker, I find Robert's fascination with landscapes and the words which we use (in many languages) to name and connect with them hugely inspiring. After a brief correspondence on Twitter and email, I approached him about an idea for a possible collaboration – to which he replied that *"something wonderful has fallen out of a clear blue sky in the past fortnight that might just be the perfect way for us to cross paths creatively"*.

And indeed it was.

Spell Songs has, quite simply, been a joy to work on. *The Lost Words* already had a special place in our household – my daughters fell in love with it the moment they saw it. To have had the opportunity to meet Jackie Morris and watch her paint whilst we made music in response to the book was both inspiring and energising. When she paints, she conjures creatures and characters with magical grace and skill. Such are their talents, that both she and Rob make their art seem effortless.

That initial walk up Cat Bells in Cumbria was the perfect environment in which to meet one another and connect. For me, it's where I love to be most. Out in the wilds – walking, climbing, running, thinking, creating. Working with Jackie, Rob, this incredible band of musicians and the supportive team behind the scenes has been a heartfelt privilege.

seckou keita

Virtuoso kora player, griot (praise singer), composer,
djembe master, solo artist and prolific collaborator

---

*Seckou's solo work reveals his exceptional skill on
the kora and his collaborations leap over cultural
barriers, discovering unforeseen affinities. He is
counted among the most influential contemporary
kora players. He himself is a source of great
inspiration with generations of musical history
informing his playing and we are overjoyed
that he is a member of Spell Songs.*

SECKOU KEITA

I first met Adam and Caroline through my appearances at Folk By The Oak. Once, they kindly let me store my double neck kora in the Armoury at Hatfield House when I was on tour in France!

I am a great fan of *The Lost Words* book and have long admired the illustrations of Jackie Morris, so I was delighted to finally get to meet her in person for the first time at The Hay Festival in May 2018, and to meet Robert Macfarlane at our London show in February 2019.

The loss of our natural habitat really resonated with me.

Back home in Senegal, Zircon mining in Casamance in the south, by big international companies, is threatening the natural landscape and with it the habitats of thousands of birds, animals and plants. Zircon is a mineral found in the sand and used in the making of mobile phones. To mine for Zircon, hundreds of acres of coastal environments and dune networks will be destroyed.

It's hard to imagine the emotional impact of losing whole stretches of your natural landscape – that which defines your own habitat. It's not just your shelter or something that your physical existence depends on, it's your emotional attachment to your landscape and the place in the world that you call home. When it's gone, you will never get it back. Your landscape, your horizon, is irreplaceable.

The avian theme has carried throughout my two albums with Catrin Finch.

Our debut album was called *Clychau Dibon*, 'Clychau' being the Welsh word for 'bells', and 'Dibon' the name of the Abyssinian hornbill, a bird native to the mangroves and wetlands of West Africa. The calls between male and female hornbills are so distinctive they have worked their ways into the rhythms and melodies of the local traditional songs.

Our second album *SOAR* was inspired by the osprey's migration between Wales (where Catrin grew up) and Senegal (where I grew up). We couldn't believe this amazing natural connection when we discovered it. These birds fly on their own between the two countries to find food, safety and a mate – no one shows them the way – and yet inherently they know where to go, and then when to make the 3000-mile journey back again. No borders, no visas, no restrictions.

Transparent Water, my recent album with Cuban jazz pianist Omar Sosa, refers to water as one of the most fundamental, natural and essential elements on Earth. Clean water should be every human's right.

The impact of technology on our lives is at the same time one of the greatest positives and yet perhaps one of the biggest threats to our traditional culture. It changes our human behaviours and interactions, as well as how we react and interact with our natural environment. Staring at a screen has replaced what may before have been shared story time with family. In griot culture where knowledge and culture is passed on aurally from generation to generation we are, for the first time, facing a real threat to this way of life.

Jim molyneux

Drummer, percussionist, pianist and keyboard player, accordion player,
singer, songwriter, composer and producer

It is not only Jim Molyneux's prodigious talent in so many instruments and his experience as a producer that made him so important for the Spell Songs collaboration; we were also impressed with his mastery of many musical genres from classical and folk to jazz and hip hop. It was fascinating to see how he drew upon all these talents and experiences to enrich the music of Spell Songs.

JIM MOLYNEUX

When Neil Pearson first emailed me about being involved in *Spell Songs*, I asked him who else was involved in the project. When he replied with the ludicrous stellar list of musicians that you hear on this album, I can't say it took me long at all to reply, with words to the effect of "YES PLEASE."

Although I have been involved in folk music, I actually spend most of my time writing and playing music in other styles; jazz, pop, theatre shows, electronic: or pretty much anything else I can get my hands on to survive as a freelance musician. You could also say that this line up of musicians are artists who you would associate with the folk idiom, yet we all have influences outside of this too, and consequentially we have made an album that is harder to categorise than just attributing the word folk to it. It draws from a pool of music which is the sum of all of our styles and influences, but mostly it draws from nature and from the beautiful work of Jackie and Robert, and the book *The Lost Words*.

I grew up in Littleborough, in Lancashire, and spent my younger years living on a sheep farm which sits snugly near the Pennines. Though I now live and work in London, I still consider it to be my home there; much of the music I have written through the years is informed by that landscape, and this album has felt like a welcome opportunity to write more music informed by those places.

Each musician in the group has a very distinctive voice, but we are a collaborative musical ensemble rather than a set of individuals, where each voice is allowed the space to shine.

As much as Gin and Tonics and Bloody Marys (thanks Robin) flowed throughout the residency, so did a great deal of creativity. Musical ideas were so easy to come by, and it's thanks to these brilliant musicians, writers, artists, curators and creators who I am honoured to join!

rachel newton

Singer, composer, harpist, fiddle and viola player, and prolific collaborator

Rachel Newton was a member of one of our previous folk music collaborations – The Elizabethan Session, and we were thrilled when she accepted our invitation to join Spell Songs. An exceptional harpist, singer and composer, her generous creativity reverberates through her collaborations and her sensitivity to word and music shines through her solo work.

RACHEL NEWTON

Collaboration is something I dearly love to do, but I always feel a sense of trepidation before starting a project such as this. A looming sense of anxiety of the unknown, the worry that we won't work well together as a group and won't have any chemistry. The fact that *The Lost Words* was already so well loved made this an even more daunting prospect than usual – we really wanted to do it justice with our music. An hour into the first day and all of these worries had evaporated. The generosity of my fellow musicians was such that we were all able to install our own individual musical characters into the music while also creating a sound that was truly ours together as a band. The fact that Rob and Jackie had made us feel so at ease and free in what we could do with their work and how we could interpret it gave us a freedom and a confidence to be creative without holding back. And we certainly didn't hold back! By the fourth day in the house we had more songs than we could fit on an album and we were really excited with how it was sounding. Having Jackie there in the house with us watching, listening, drawing and occasionally dropping in an invaluable little gem of information or comment really informed our work. I was fortunate enough to witness Jackie create the incredible egret on harp while we were all together. Watching her create that piece of work was a true highlight of this project and among the many occasions over the *Spell Songs* process that I've shed a good few happy tears.

karine polwart

Singer, songwriter and musician, theatre maker, storyteller and author

---

Robert Macfarlane picked out Karine's script for her award winning show Wind Resistance for The Guardian's BEST BOOKS of 2017. The appreciation of each other's work is mutual and, naturally, we were eager for her to be a part of Spell Songs and overjoyed when she accepted our invitation.

KARINE POLWART

I fell in love with Jackie's mythic worlds when my kids were little, and eventually told her so on Facebook, only to be informed in return that she sometimes plays my songs as she paints! With her permission, I've borrowed one of her wrens as my Facebook profile pic. Such is the 21st-century way. A Jackie Morris print of a woman holding a barn owl (in Scottish Gaelic, cailleach-oidhche gheal or the white old woman of the night), keeps watch in my living room at home, opposite the shelves which host Rob's *The Old Ways* and *Landmarks*.

The Lost Words arrived in my home via a friend who gifted a copy to each of several pals simultaneously. So many words within it are heart stuff. I sang my kids to sleep with songs of "bonnie, bloomin heather" and "Scotch bluebells". My record label *hegri* borrows the Shetlandic word for heron. My workspace is at Saughland Farm, named after the old Scots word for willow.

From my studio, I can see Fala Moor, the peatbog epicentre of my theatre work *Wind Resistance* and my album, *A Pocket of Wind Resistance* (crafted with Pippa Murphy). Both speak and sing of the landscape and life around me, not least the little astronaut larks. I was astonished when Rob chose these two combined works as his 2017 "book of the year".

In old lore, the nimbleness and guile of the wren trumps the might of the eagle in a flying contest to become The King of Birds. It's a story about the power of what's wee and commonplace. I'm honoured to be the wren's human embodiment on these pages. Small, clear-voiced and quite fierce, I think Jackie might have said. I'll take that.

I'm delighted too, to be one amongst many in this beautiful *Spell Songs* chorus of musicians, writers, makers, bakers, thinkers, drivers, and engineers. Thanks to everyone.

beth porter

Cellist, singer, songwriter, violinist and ukulele player

To add depth and range to the ensemble we invited Beth Porter, a superb cellist and singer, to be a part of Spell Songs. We were drawn to her work on numerous collaborations from a variety of different musical genres as well as her involvement in The Bookshop Band where she expertly turns literature into song. A sensational cellist with a timeless voice.

BETH PORTER

We were given *The Lost Words* as a Christmas present in 2017 just after we moved to Dumfries and Galloway. What a stunning gift! We hadn't heard of the book before but my dad was a Robert Macfarlane fan and we knew that Jackie Morris had links to Bath (where we used to live) and had seen her work on the walls in Mr B's Emporium of Reading Delights Bookshop. Little did I know what was to come! When I first met Rob in the Lake District we found that we had some friends in common including Stanley Donwood. I used to teach his daughter the cello! Jackie then told me that she sometimes listens to The Bookshop Band while she works and I felt like we were all old friends. I write a lot of songs inspired by books in The Bookshop Band with my husband Ben Please so I'm used to delving into literature for inspiration. I have particularly enjoyed books that link to nature including *The Snow Goose* by Paul Gallico and *The Snow Geese* by William Fiennes. What I hadn't done before was immerse myself in beautiful art to inspire song. The collaboration between artist, writer and musicians in this project made for an enriching, creative and moving experience. When I was asked to do *Spell Songs* I honestly felt humbled and honoured (and a little scared!) to be part of such a creative group of talented song-writers and musicians. They listened, they played beautifully and were a joy to be around. In our everyday lives, even as musicians it is easy to get caught up in ourselves and our work. This was an opportunity to weave the outside world and nature into our work and has inspired me to do so in future song-writing and composing.

My cello belonged to my Great Aunt Diana who played when she was younger. When she died, it was discovered that it still belonged to the family and eventually came to me to play. It was made in 1794. Seeing Jackie delicately paint the cello and surround it in a charm of goldfinches brought a new dimension to the history and beauty of the instrument. Charm on, Goldfinch, Charm on.

INSTRUMENTAL CREDITS

KERRY ANDREW
VOCALS, MELODICA

KRIS DREVER
VOCALS, ACOUSTIC GUITAR, ELECTRIC GUITAR, BASS GUITAR

JULIE FOWLIS
VOCALS, SHRUTI BOX, WHISTLES

SECKOU KEITA
VOCALS, KORA

JIM MOLYNEUX
VOCALS, PIANO, RHODES, SYNTHS, ACCORDION, DRUMS, PERCUSSION

RACHEL NEWTON
VOCALS, ELECTROHARP, FIDDLE, VIOLA

KARINE POLWART
VOCALS, TENOR GUITAR, INDIAN HARMONIUM

BETH PORTER
VOCALS, WHISTLING, CELLO, UKULELE

PRODUCED BY **ANDY BELL**
ENGINEERED & MIXED BY **ANDY BELL**
ASSISTANT ENGINEER | **JOE JONES**
MASTERED BY **DEAN HONER**

RECORDED AT ROCKFIELD STUDIOS, MONMOUTH | JANUARY 2019
MIXED AT HUDSON STUDIOS | FEBRUARY & MARCH 2019

WILDLIFE AUDIO RECORDED BY **CHRIS WATSON**
OTHER 'FOUND SOUND' AUDIO RECORDED
AROUND MONMOUTH BY **JOE JONES**

►Would you hew me to the heartwood, cutter, hear my sap's mutter. Leave me nothing but a mutter. Mark my heartbeat, breaker of rocks, a heap of logs—Drinker of rain, breath-giver, deep-thinker, time-keeper, maker of life—Put an ear to my bark, cutter, hear my sap's country of creatures! But my world takes seconds to crash.▼Do you hear me low.▼Have those words called you, cutter? Have I sent you... Who... Your saw takes years to grow. I am a pile of brash, a pile of shade, enter of shade... cutter, bitter, I am a world, cutter. Would you leave me the open-hearted? Would you turn me to timber, cutter?

❓

HEARTWOOD

Would you hew me to
    the heartwood, cutter?
Would you lay me low
    beneath your feet?
Listen to my sap mutter
Hear my heartwood beat

Would you throw me on
    the log pile, cutter?
Would you toss me to
    the steel saw blade?
Listen to my leaves flutter
Hear my heartwood break

Would you lean your back
    against me, cutter?
Would you rest your axe
    a while and sleep?
Listen to this song I utter.
Hear my heartwood weep

Hear my heartwood
Heartwood
Hear my heartwood

I drink the rain
I eat the sun
I gift the breath that fills your lungs
I hear the roaring engine thrum
But I cannot run

Would you hew me to
    the heartwood, cutter?
Would you lay me low
    beneath your feet?
Listen to my sap mutter
Hear my heartwood beat

Hear my heartwood
Heartwood
Hear my heartwood

This is a turning and whittling of Robert's 'charm against harm' (depicted here as a golden spiral of writing), which he wrote in response to the unjust felling of trees, particularly on the streets of Sheffield. It's a spell in praise of trees, not in blame of woodcutters (who know more about trees than anyone else, when they do need to come down). **Karine Polwart**

SELKIE-BOY

Go now selkie-boy, swim from the shore,
Rinse your ears clean of human chatter,
And empty your bones of heather
   and moor,
And your mind of human matter.

Hear us and hasten
High are our voices
Offering welcome, and keening our joy
High are our voices
Offering welcome
And drawing you down to where
   you belong.

Selkie, selkie-boy, come join your kin,
Eager your kind are to meet you,
As salt sets its seal on your silky skin
Let green sea rise up to greet you.

Hear us and hasten
High are our voices

Offering welcome, and keening our joy
High are our voices
Offering welcome
And drawing you down to where you . . .

Blue is the water – it beckons you . . .
Blue is the water

Oh selkie-boy, swim from the shore,
Rinse your ears clean of human chatter,
And empty your bones of heather
   and moor,
And your mind of its human matter.

Hear us and hasten
High are our voices
Offering welcome, and keening our joy
High are our voices
Offering welcome
And drawing you down to where
   you belong.

Songs and tales of the seal people are a big part of Hebridean folklore, especially in my home island of North Uist and in the Monach Islands. I have always been fascinated by these stories that make mention of Norse royalty, enchantment, separation and isolation, but equally I find the melodic qualities in these ethereal songs utterly mesmerising.

When Rob invited me to look at one of his new spells *Grey Seal* I was immediately drawn to it. He calls it *A Summoning Spell, A Drowning Song*. Like a true folksong, it is both heart-breaking and beautiful at the same time.

Kris and I worked on this late one evening in a quiet corner, with Kris trying out riffs and chordal ideas. As soon as he played the opening chord sequence you can hear in the *Selkie-boy*, I knew that was the one. I took it away and set the melody to Rob's words that night, and the group further shaped it the next day by adding their own magic to it. Julie Fowlis

KINGFISHER

Kingfisher: the colour giver, fire
    bringer, flame-flicker, river's quiver.

Ink-black bill, orange throat,
    and a quick blue back-gleaming
    feather-stream.

Neat and still it sits on the snag
    of a stick, until with . . .

Gold-flare, wing-fan, whipcrack the
    kingfisher – *zingfisher, singfisher!* –

Flashes down too fast to follow, quick
    and quicker carves its hollow

In the water, slings its arrow
    superswift to swallow

Stickleback or shrimp or minnow.

Halcyon is its other name –
    also ripple-calmer, water-nester,

Evening angler, weather-teller,
    rainbringer and

Rainbow bird – that sets the
    stream alight with burn and glitter!

Halcyon, sets the stream alight.

O Rainbow bird.

Rainbringer, weather-teller.

Before we got together to start writing the music for *Spell Songs* I hit upon the idea of creating short and immediate improvisations in reaction to Jackie Morris's artwork in the book. The rules were, no rehearsal, no peeking beforehand, no corrections and nothing longer than a minute. It was a way to start musical conversations in case we found ourselves confronted with blank pages. I put them in a shared folder and alerted everyone else to their presence.

I think it was Julie who said that she liked the *Kingfisher* improv early on the first writing day, so we all started playing it. Before we stopped grooving the first time round we'd written a top line and Kerry had words for it. If you have a group of committed musicians sometimes that's enough right?

The original idea was a response to the painting – quickness, brightness, flashing, sparks and colour. Once you associate a piece of music with an image it always seems like it was intended but in this case I suppose it genuinely was. Rainbow Bird.

Kris Drever

HERON

Here hunts heron, here hunts heron
wreaked from blue
Here hunts heron, here hunts heron
a grey-winged weapon
Here hunts heron, here hunts heron
beaked with steel
Here hunts heron, here hunts heron
eked from iron
Here hunts heron, here hunts heron

Rock still at weir sill. Stone still at weir sill.
Dead still at weir sill. Still still at weir sill.

Ni yé Kounan koy djé fali nooma
issa lon ko nisso tidjé ye
Ni yé Kounan koy djé fali nooma
issa lon ko nisso tidjé ye
nisso tidié yeh kounan koy té bola fali
noma yeh
nisso

Here hunts heron, here hunts heron…

Now heron hauls himself into flight.
Steady wingbeats through evening light.

Kounan koy djé fali nooma
issa lon ko nisso tidjé yeh
Ni yé Kounan koy djé fali noma
nisso tidié yeh
aaah nisso yiii aaah nisso tidié yeh
Kounan koy djé fali nooma
nisso tidié yeh
kounan koy

TRANSLATED FROM MANDINKA:
If you see a heron sitting on top of a donkey,
then the cow is missing!

Herons are very common back in Senegal. We have brown and white herons who are commonly seen standing on the backs of cows as they graze.

We have a saying in Mandinka which goes, 'If you see a heron sitting on top of a donkey, then the cow is missing'. So I sang this line over the top of the melody.

The melody was created out of the swinging motion of the cow as it walks; the rhythm mimics the action of the bird marching on top of the cow. **Seckou Keita**

LITTLE ASTRONAUT

Little Astronaut,
   where have you gone?
And how is your song
   still torrenting on?

Are you short of breath
   up there in thin air
Your magical song
   still tumbling on?

Right now I need you
Right now I need you
Right now I need you,
   for my sadness has come again.

My heart it grows flatter,
   so I'm coming to find you,
Coming to find you by
   following your song.

Right now I need you
Right now I need you
Right now I need you,
   for my sadness has come again.

Keeping on to deep space,
   past dying stars and suns,
Little astronaut sing
Little astronaut sing

Right now I need you
Right now I need you
Right now I need you,
   for my sadness has come again.

Little astronaut,
   where have you gone?
And how is your song
   still torrenting on?

Myself, Kris and Seckou created this song on the second morning of our residency in Herefordshire. It felt as if the words of *Lark* went from the page, to our eyes, our minds, and back out via our mouths in song in a matter of around half an hour or so; the creative process of assembling the poem into song was a quick and natural one.

The population of the skylark halved during the 90s, and has declined further since, but despite this you can still hear them high above Blackstone Edge, which is the name of the gritstone escarpment in the South Pennines near to where I grew up.

"Keeping on into deep space, past dying stars and exploding suns, to where at last, little astronaut, you sing out your heart at all dark matter." From the entire book, this line speaks to me the most, and I believe that in a sense it defines *Spell Songs*. We live in a time of loss, of life and of language. As musicians, when we come by dark matter, we are able to sing of / at it, which is a greatly cathartic process, but as Robert mentioned, is also the most beautiful way to combat darkness. On this album you hear we eight musicians singing our hearts out at all dark matter, and this song is a nod to all voices – small or great, loud or lonely– who do the same. Jim Molyneux

ACORN

As flake is to blizzard, as

Curve is to sphere, as
knot is to net, as

One is to many, as
coin is to money, as
bird is to flock, as

Rock is to mountain, as
drop is to fountain, as
spring is to river, as
glint is to glitter, as

Near is to far, as
wind is to weather, as
feather is to flight, as
light is to star, as
kindness is to good,
so acorn is to wood.

Before we came together in
Monnington House, Kris had been
playing around with every spell, adding
a few short improvisations as a direct
reaction to each one. He sent these
to us to listen to. Something about
his *Acorn* improvisations inspired the
melody I came up with for the song.
The words in this particular spell just
fit so well as a song already and I didn't
change anything lyrically. The melody
came to me pretty much immediately
as I was singing through the words
for the first time. A version of Kris'
improvisation introduces the song
on this recording. **Rachel Newton**

GHOST OWL

Silence
all silence
owl hunts in silence

Sound
all sound
owl hunts the sound

Run
for cover
all run
for cover

Run
for cover
all run
for cover

Will you listen with owl ears for a while?
    (ghost owl)

Will you listen with owl ears for a while?
    (ghost owl)

I came to the residency after three weeks of extreme illness, and had to leave after a day and a half having made myself rather worse. It was still a gloriously creative few hours for me; I'd been nervous to see how eight diverse personalities might mix, but found with pleasure how kind, giving and musically flexible everyone was. Things happened so naturally, without force. After a night of little sleep, feeling a shell of myself, I sat on the sofa in deepest Herefordshire, with Jim, Beth, Rachel also in the room, looking over Rob's words for a spell about a barn owl. Jim began playing these gorgeous, doomy chords on his keyboard – Massive Attack meets the soundtrack to *The Bridge* – and I began singing. The ladies joined in – eerie 'cello harmonics and a steady, tense droplet effect on the electric harp. With Rob's words on my lap, I teased out the ones that felt most song lyric-like.

    Jim looked up other names for barn owl on his phone: white owl, silver owl, demon owl, night owl, delicate owl, hobby owl, church owl, ghost owl. It is a portentous bird, once believed to bring ruin, its moon-grave face infusing dread, but it's always been one of my favourites: I once held one at Lambeth Country Show in South London, holding my breath at the same time. On a recent episode of the BBC's *Winterwatch*, there was a test to measure the noise made by a kestrel and a barn owl as they flew: the kestrel's wings made the slightest whisper, but the barn owl was utterly silent. It is capable of making no sound at all. This song is about the hush of the hunt, and the dread and the inevitability of the prey that cannot hear it.

Singing this song felt like a gift for me: there's nothing I like more than being breathy and spectral! I had to leave the residency far too soon; but my ghost owl stayed with me, hovering. **Kerry Andrew**

THE SNOW HARE

The hare turns white as
  the year turns black
O the rain is falling
The hare turns white as
  the year turns black
O the dark is rising

By the Loch of the Birds, he
  hunkers down in the heather.
He waits for the veil of snow to
  come and cover him over.

The snow hare hides in
  the mountain moss
O the sleet is falling
The snow hare hides in
  the mountain moss
O the dark is rising

By the Cairn of the Goose, he
  hunkers down in the heather.
He longs for the veil of snow to
  come and cover him over.

The hare he waits on the
  highest hill but the
  snow is no more falling
The hare he waits
  on the highest hill
O the dark is rising

By the Rock of the Stag,
  he shelters in from
  the weather.
He prays for the veil
  of snow to come
  and cover him over.

If knowing the names, the words, for creatures, birds and plants allows us to see, and to care for, what's actually there, it's true also that what's actually there has, in many cases, altered beyond all recognition in recent decades. In the UK, vast tumbling murmurations of starlings (one of the "lost words") are no longer commonplace because the population has declined by two thirds since the 1970s. Numbers of skylarks declined by half during the 1990s alone, largely due to intensive farming practices. Both birds are now red-listed endangered species.

    The mountain hare is the only truly Arctic animal of Scotland, and it is also under threat due to rapid ecological shifts. A creature that has evolved winter camouflage becomes immensely vulnerable when the snows don't come as they used to. This song, led by Julie and Karine, speaks to that fragility.

Parallels can be drawn too, to the fragility of the Gaelic language which so often names the places which the mountain hare inhabits. Julie last saw a mountain hare when climbing Ben Gulabin in Perthshire and this provided added inspiration for the song. The place names on the map nearby are beautiful and descriptive; Ben Gulabin itself means 'Hill of the Curlew' and within close proximity you will find names such as Loch nan Eun (Loch of the Birds) and Càrn a' Gheòidh (Cairn of the Goose).

A snow hare sits in the opening pages of *The Lost Words*, to symbolise Robert Macfarlane himself, a man who loves and needs the mountains. **Julie Fowlis and Karine Polwart**

CONKER (MAGIC CASKET)

Cabinet-maker, could you craft me a conker?

Oil its wood, burnish its veneer, set it glowing
from within?

Never. Not a chance. No hope at all.

King, then, could you command me a conker?
Compel its green spikes to grow, its white plush
To thicken? *Impossible. Impractical. Inconceivable.*

Engineer, surely you could design me a conker?
Refine its form, mill its curves and edges?
Manufacture me that magic casket?
Unfeasible. Unworkable. Unimaginable.

Realise this (said the Cabinet-maker, the King and
the Engineer together), *conker cannot be made,*
however you ask it, whatever word or tool you use,
regardless of decree. Only one thing can conjure
conker – and that thing is tree.

Conker cannot be made. But songs and stories can. And so too can, and
must, new ways of being and living with the non-human life all around us.
Our collective survival depends upon it. And the survival of much else
besides. Whatever is to come next will start by being imagined. It's being
imagined somewhere already right now. And these fledgling imaginings, as
they emerge, will undoubtedly be dismissed also as impossible, unworkable,
unfeasible, as all change is until it happens. **Karine Polwart**

PAPA KÉBA

Seckou:
Kounung killii bila
até dan-kungnaa
kou djama léh yélémata-wo
papa kéba aaa

eeyéee papa kéba ba
kou djama léh yélémata
djamani koura
Séné-Gambia lee finn bii
    fongkau enndaï
woyé kouma djama lé bitiwo
    djamani koura

Julie:
An rud a thèid fad o'n t-sùil
Thèid e fad o'n chridhe

An nì nach eil caillte, gheibhear e

Seckou:
kounung killii bila
Até dankung na
kou djama léh yélémata-wo
papa ké ba

Julie:
An nì nach eil caillte, gheibhear e

Seckou:
kouma djama léh yélémata-wo
papa ké ba

TRANSLATED FROM MANDINKA:
You call yesterday's name in vain,

*If you call yesterday today he will
    not answer you.*

*So much has changed papa kéba;
    Oh papa kéba so many words
    have been lost.*

*What secrets are contained
    through the expression of
    our words in Diola, or in
    Manding – the expression
    of the dominant language
    erases the words of others.*

TRANSLATED FROM GAELIC:
*What goes far from the eye
Will go far from the heart*

What is not lost, can be found.

Papa Kéba is a song I brought from my own world to meet *The Lost Words* book. *Papa Kéba* translates as Elder Father, and I play it in an ancient style, a style of playing I haven't used in a long time. Julie Fowlis was keen for us to work together on something in our own languages (Mandinka and Gaelic).

I told Julie about a saying we have in Mandinka; 'If you call yesterday today it won't answer', i.e. if you try to summon up the past it won't answer. Julie responded with a Gaelic saying which was very similar, 'Something your eye doesn't see your heart won't feel.'

What we're saying is that a lot of words have changed direction with the new generation. Old words get buried, or local words get replaced by new colonial or even global terms. You need to dig to find the old words. **Seckou Keita**

CHARM ON, GOLDFINCH

All along the bay
Where the old railway
Used to lie
You can find

A martyr in a marsh
It's a path we take
Goldfinch in its wake
Gilds with grace

Spring-tide high
Red head you fly
In and out of sight
Little gifts of light

Tracks forever change
And the season fades
Goodbye to the sun
Goodbye Golden One

Charm on Goldfinch, charm on
Heaven help us when all your
   gold is gone
Charm on Goldfinch, charm on
Heaven help us when all your
   gold is gone

These lyrics are partly inspired by my regular walks in Wigtown along the Martyrs' Stake where I see goldfinches along the path and in the trees. It's beautiful with a view of the old harbour, Galloway Hills and marshes but it has a darker tale too. Two women, Margaret Lachlan, 60, and Margaret Wilson, 18, were Scottish Covenanters who were drowned on stakes by Scottish Episcopalians in the marshes as the tide came up in 1685. Apparently they were pardoned but the news came too late. The goldfinch lights up this track and gilds the way even on the darker days.

The chorus 'Charm on, Goldfinch, charm on / Heaven help us when all your gold is gone' is from Robert's spell. He wrote the poem whilst sitting with his 101-year-old grandmother during her last few days of life. **Beth Porter**

I had always wanted to do something with *Willow*, partly because it's the spell I read out loud when we all first got together in the Lakes. I love the line 'Lean in, listeners'. Listening was such a huge part of our work in this collaboration. It has been a very generous process. While we were in Monnington House making the music, it was Karine who, knowing I was keen on the spell, alerted me to the fact that Seckou was in the other room having a play through some ideas for *Willow*. I sat listening to his melody and came up with the idea for the song to go with it. Rachel Newton

WILLOW

Willow, when the wind blows
Whisper while we listen so we learn what
   words your long leaves loosen

Whisper, when the wind blows
Listen for a day, a week 'til we know what
   the willows say, what willows speak

Lean in, oh listeners
Listen for a week, a day, but you will
   never hear what willows say

Open up your heartwood
Show your deep within, your rough
   without, your water brushing bough,
your shoot, your grain, your knot

Yiro té séla a diambo-la sunguo léba laa
fonio lé ka fé

Yiro té séla a diambo-la sunguo léba laa
fonio lé ka fé
fonio ow owo fonio

Willow, when the wind blows
Whisper while we listen so we learn what
   words your long leaves loosen

Whisper, when the wind blows
Listen for a day, a week 'til we know what
   the willows say, what willows speak

Lean in, oh listeners
Listen for a week, a day, but you will
   never hear what willows say

Open up your heartwood
Show your deep within, your rough
   without, your water brushing bough,
your shoot, your grain, your knot

Yiro té séla a diambo-la sunguo léba laa
fonio lé ka fé
nima lamoy ita moyla

Yiro té séla a diambo-la sunguo léba laa
nima lamoy fonio lé ka fé
eeey yé ey

Willow, when the wind blows.

TRANSLATED FROM MANDINKA:

You can't climb a tree by its leaves.
   You have to start with the trunk.

It's the wind that makes the leaves move,
   to hear that you have to listen harder,
   to hear the music in the leaves.

SCATTERSEED

Spin me round, tiny time machine,
They used to call you Lion's Tooth or Windblow,
They used to call you Milkwitch or Parachute,
They used to call you Evening Glow.

Scatterseed, Scatterseed,
The fallen star of the football field,

Let new names take, let them thrive and grow,
Dazzle me you little sun of the grass,
I hear you roaring 'Death to lawn perfection',
The timepiece no longer known as

Scatterseed, Scatterseed,
The fallen star of the football field,
Scatterseed, Scatterseed,
I'd never call you 'just a weed'.

My childhood area of expertise was football and the football fields of my childhood glow brightly in my memory. An endless, timeless syrup of the state now known as mindfulness. I can remember lying on my belly on those pitches in distraction, when the kickabout had disintegrated into some other group fantasy. I remember the tangy taste of daisy stalks and the little lion's manes that stuck up from the flat, the biggest points of geographical interest on that micro tableau. I remember seeing it as the cityscape of the tiny creatures (that only kiddos regularly spot) and getting lost there. It's impossibly romantic in my recollection, clichéd even, but there it is. It's part of me.

Childhood memories and actual children are the reality now but what I remember is that little things can have huge significance. It's why *Dandelion* in *The Lost Words* spoke to me so strongly, the dandelion is a toy, a tower, a clock, a lion, a parachute, a crayon, a flower, an accessory, a renegade and one of the unsung heroes of every childhood. **Kris Drever**

I suggested the idea of a blessing that borrows images and phrases from many of
The Lost Words spells (*Bluebell, Dandelion, Fern, Heather, Heron, Kingfisher, Lark, Otter,
Raven* and *Starling*), as well as from new spells (*Goldfinch* and *Grey Seal*). The form is
inspired by blessings in Scottish Gaelic, particularly from a beautiful collection of charms
and incantations called *Carmina Gadelica*. Many of the old blessings invoke local landscapes
and a litany of non-human life. And many are framed as lullabies. We gathered our blessing
together round Jim's piano in just over an hour. And we offer it both in hope and light,
and in grief for the losses and dark times yet to come. **Karine Polwart**

THE LOST WORDS BLESSING

Enter the wild with care, my love
And speak the things you see
Let new names take and root and thrive and grow
And even as you travel far from heather, crag and river
May you like the little fisher, set the stream alight with glitter
May you enter now as otter without falter into water

Look to the sky with care, my love
And speak the things you see
Let new names take and root and thrive and grow
And even as you journey on past dying stars exploding
Like the gilded one in flight, leave your little gifts of light
And in the dead of night my darling, find the gleaming eye of starling
Like the little aviator, sing your heart to all dark matter

Walk through the world with care, my love
And sing the things you see
Let new names take and root and thrive and grow
And even as you stumble through machair sands eroding
Let the fern unfurl your grieving, let the heron still your breathing
Let the selkie swim you deeper, oh my little silver-seeker
Even as the hour grows bleaker, be the singer and the speaker
And in city and in forest, let the larks become your chorus
And when every hope is gone, let the raven call you home

IN CONVERSATION

JACKIE MORRIS + DAVID WEIR

What follows is an interview which appeared on the Folk Radio UK website in
May 2019 between David Weir and Jackie Morris.

David: So first of all I'd like to say a big thank you for *The Lost Words: A Spell*
Book. This *Spell Songs* project looked like such a joy to be a part of.

    Robert's opening comment for his recent Guardian piece, "it felt like the
folk music equivalent of Avengers Assemble" tickled me as I'd thought just
the same. There's such an undeniable mystery and magic surrounding the
book, how did it feel working so closely and watching the musicians 'take the
spells deeper into the soul' and seeing how they all interpreted the material?

Jackie: From the very first moment when we were contacted by our agent
and asked about this project it has felt rather like a dream. I listened to Karine
as I worked on the book. Beth and The Bookshop Band have travelled with me
for a long time in my van, and Seckou has been in my life for many years also.
All of the musicians have provided a soundtrack to my working life, so to be
working with them is astonishing.

    Listening to them shaping the music from the silent intimacy of reading
and looking has been an education.

David: I was really interested to read about the book's relation to end of life/older-
life communities and in dementia cases. Many of my fondest memories as a
child were spent with my Grandfather (who worked for National Geographic for
a spell) as he taught me the names of the various countryside flora and fauna.
Now we're able to share that again; I see someone who evidently struggles with
names and faces, vividly recalling creatures and plants by their Latin names.

It reminded me of music's power to trigger memories in dementia/ Alzheimer's cases. Then there is the book's amazing influence in deprived areas of Britain. As you said, it is without a doubt a book "for people, not for children". I was wondering if you have any favourite instances of how the book has reached people in different ways and how this feels to be a part of?

Jackie: Almost every day Robert and I are sent stories about children, reluctant to read, who spend hours in the pages of our book, about children who have turned away from screentime into the book. Robert's spells have been read at weddings and funerals.

 A woman wrote to me and said she had come to the UK to see her 95 year old father. She lives in Australia now and he has been living with Alzheimer's, and they thought he had reached the stage where his language had gone. He'd not spoken for a long while. She gave him a copy of the book and he slowly turned the pages, becoming more absorbed. When he reached the bramble page he began to talk about blackbirds, about his childhood in Dorset, and later when shown a picture of his wife he remembered her name.

 Many people have said they've spent rich time with their parents, older relatives, in the pages of the book.

 A 98 year old woman said she had bought one to share with her great grandchild. She had 19 of them (great grandchildren – as she pointed out as 19 of the books would be very heavy for a 98 year old woman to carry), but this one, well, she loves the natural world, she said. 98, fierce bright and loving life.

 People have found refuge in the pages of our book at the end of their lives and what a compliment that is, when you know how little time you have left but you spend it in the book.

The book has brought us new friends, like Joe, like Diane, who found a place to breathe, a scent of the wild in it.

What does that feel like? It leaves you lost for words. Sometimes broken, but always mended. And every person who brings such a story teaches us more. There's no one favourite. It's overwhelming, utterly overwhelming, in a good way, beautiful.

Stitch music in to the soul of the book and I hope together we can reach more people.

David: "People are using the book, every day, and every day teaching us more about it." This 'beautiful protest' of yours certainly doesn't seem to be losing any traction. Often when musicians discuss the release of a new album, they talk about the music becoming public domain and ultimately an unpredictable force that then moves beyond them.

I was wondering how you felt about the cultural phenomenon of *The Lost Words* now? It has a wildness of its own, there's a genuine sense these spells cast might will more creatures into existence – one fan shared "My awareness was heightened. I know people call this 'frequency illusion'. I call it natural magic!"

With it crossing disciplines and reaching diverse audiences how do you feel the record and live performances might take it further? Do you feel its reception also suggests a wider recognition in people that they do feel disconnected from the natural world? It seems more common in general, is it now more important than ever to remedy that?

Jackie: I think there is a realisation growing that nature isn't something apart from us, but that we are a small, infinitely small, part of it. I think the book is part of a forest of books that attempt to focus attention onto the more than human. I know that music can take it deeper.

The aim of the book was to change focus, to bring into light the everyday, close by, natural world. What is under the nose isn't always noticed.

The aim of the music, I hope, is to take these spells deeper into people's hearts and souls. Music and memory link in such strong ways. New stories, new songs, I think we are all hungry for this.

David: I find it fascinating the ways in which folk music and environmental protest can intersect, as Macfarlane put it "Folk tradition's long double allegiance to landscape and protest aligns precisely with the book's own purpose." Many artists are harnessing the power of song as a form of 'Abstract Activism' as Sam Lee referred to it when promoting his *Singing With Nightingales* project. We've seen Jim Aldridge & Sid Goldsmith up in arms, Rowan Piggott with his bee-lore & folksong: *Songhive* project and of course Karine's wonderful *Wind Resistance*. Do you feel folk music and more art in general might develop this stronger environmental conscience, or rather is it more where you look for it and how you read into art that is already out there?

Jackie: I grew up with the songs of Leon Rosselson, Ewan MacColl, Dick Gaughan and later Rory McCleod and others. They taught me history, as well as protest. They taught me about land rights and trespass. They taught me about other singers in other countries.

I'm not sure *Spell Songs* is folk music. In the way that *The Lost Words* isn't a children's book, rather a book for people, the *Spell Songs* is also out of any category. It is music, shaped around the book, but wilder, sung from the heart, and I hope that it will reach out to people. In these times I think we all need a lifeline. I met someone not so long ago who had come from the USA to see *The Lost Words* exhibition. She said Robert's work was almost all that was keeping her going through The Trump Years. She was in tears. *Spell Songs* is for people like her. A sonic haven.

David: Following on from that, in Daegan Miller's interview for Public Books, Macfarlane suggests: "Perhaps we shouldn't think of books as saving the world, but rather as catalysing uncountable small unknown acts of good - to think about the ways in which small acts can together, cumulatively, grow into change. In this way we might think of writing as like the work of a coral reef, slowly building its structures through many small interventions, rather than like a single thunderclap or silver bullet. You always are threatened by quietism, but I think that to give up for the lack of a silver bullet is wasteful."

Sometimes it can seem difficult to stand your ground against the pressures of climate change and the cavalier actions of certain politicians. I was wondering how you felt about literature and art's power as a form of (environmental) protest in the 21st Century?

Jackie: I'm not sure how to answer this. So, this is what I can say. I paint. I have always made a living as an artist. I've been lucky in that over time my clients have been New Statesman, New Socialist, Oxfam, Greenpeace, Amnesty International, New Internationalist. When I have worked on books I have told the stories I want to tell and they have found enough of an audience for me to continue to work. I paint from the heart. I try to paint beauty and it's hard, always turning to the light in a world so filled with troubles. And I write, I paint, to try to make sense of the world. I would rather create than destroy. I can speak only for myself.

There is another thing though. As you reconnect your soul with your place in the natural world you realise what a farce and a sham politics is and how broken is a system that sees such people in positions of governance. And yet we are stuck with this broken system and there is no way to make the best of it. We need new dreamers to find a new way, new stories to shape the future, new songs, always, new songs.

David: For the album artwork you decided to paint each musician as a creature, how naturally did this idea come about? I enjoyed hearing more on your blog; "Jim was a barn owl at first. But then he changed. He's quiet. Listens. But when he opens his mouth to sing, he has a beautiful voice. So, he's a lark." It reads like the diary of a keen birdwatcher, was there a feeling of waiting for the musician's 'spirit animal' slowly to come into focus?

Jackie: I don't think of them as the animals/birds being their 'spirit animal', rather that they are the creature's spirit person. Each person has about them something of the creature. Some are harder to find as they flit between species. Robert is the snow hare at the beginning of *The Lost Words*.

Drawing is all about looking, at the shape of a thing. These days I am watching birds, trying to catch their shape. All of the musicians became birds in my mind's eye. There's something of the raven in Kris Drever, even in the way he loves to play with effects and sounds. Karine has always been a wren. Julie was the hardest, and she flitted around shore birds until she settled as a lapwing, and now this just seems so right. There's a lightness about her, but pale skin, dark hair, a dancing grace, and colour so rich in her voice that also wavers like the flight of a peewit.

David: Obviously both Macfarlane's and your own work have deep ecological ties, was there a key moment when you felt this was something that you desperately needed to pursue and could you ever have imagined it would have this kind of impact around the time of its conception? From tending it from seed to sapling and now to its myriad branching spin-offs – do you feel there's still new ground left to be broken?

Jackie: In 2015 Robert and I walked in to the offices at Hamish Hamilton with a painting, a spell, an idea. No one really knew what this would become. It was so hard to explain what we were trying to make, but Simon Prosser, our editor, had faith in us. We hoped that what we were making would be a large and gilded spell book and over the next two years we worked, with Hermione Thompson, with Alison O'Toole, to bring it to life. In just over a year it has become a touring exhibition, a building, music in many forms, outdoor theatre, perhaps a film, always a book. Now we have eight musicians, sell out tours and this CD. Let's see what *Spell Songs* becomes.

A schools' pack by Eva John exploring the music, artwork and natural wonders found in Spell Songs is available to download from our website thelostwords.org/resources (Suitable for KS2-KS3).

Eva John has also created an inspirational school's explorer pack for The Lost Words book commissioned by The John Muir Trust which can be found on their website johnmuirtrust.org

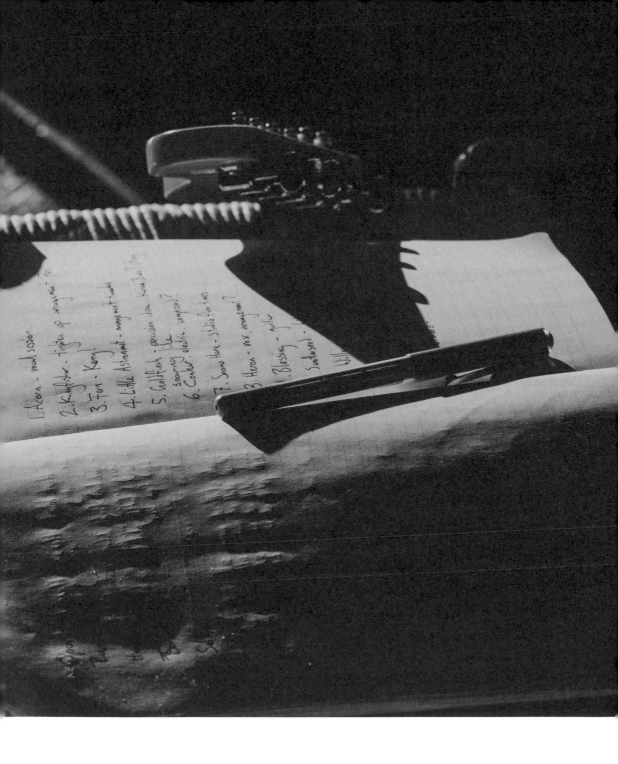

barn owl

barn owl

Below barn owl spreads silence –

All sound crouches to ground,

Runs for cover, battens down;

Noise is what owl hunts, drops on, stops dead.

Over rushes, across marshes, owl hushes –

Will you listen with owl ears for a while?

Let our world's din deafen you,
   let owl's world's whispers call you in?

egret

egret

Ever seen a brighter sight than
   little egret taking flight?

God damn you if you say you have.

Rip of paper, spill of light; none
   quite matches egret's white.

Egret out-brights marble, shows snow up
   as sullen, not-right shadow of itself.

Time flows, day slows, dark gathers – but
   egret flies on, white and low of height,
   scattering night to left and right.

goldfinch

goldfinch

God knows this world needs all the good
   it can get right now – and

Out in the gardens, the woods, goldfinches
   are gilding the land for free,

Leaving little gifts of light: a gleam for the
   teasel, a glint for the tree.

Didn't you hear their high scattered song,
   their bright twitter,

Falling around you as flecks, as grains,
   as glitter?

Imagine the loss of their lustre, the
   lack of their sheen;

No more shimmer, an unsettling absence of gilt.

Charm on, goldfinch, charm on – and

Heaven help us when all your gold is gone.

peregrine

peregrine

Peregrine is pilgrim-bird –
  world-wanderer, cloud-splitter.

Ever looked up, seen peregrine

Race sun across sky, leave
  light for dust?

Ever wondered what it must be like to

Ghost over borders, as peregrine does?

Rise from ground now, up by
  quick wing-flicks and gyre

Into air, where frontiers fade fast.

Never stop dreaming of flying
  further, higher,

Ending up where the heart hopes for,
  yearns to, at last.

snow hare

snow hare

Snow hare whitens as the year turns dark.

Night rises, rain falls as sleet on higher ground.

On moors, by tors, in peat, hare hunkers into form;

Weathers what would kill you without fight.

Hare, walking, is graceless lollop,

Awkward piston, awkward shunt.

Running, hare smooths sudden into speed,
   flows over hill-top, lee-slope —

Each quick arc a mark of hare, a sign of hope.

grey seal

grey seal

Go now selkie-boy, swim from the shore,

Rinse your ears clean of human chatter,

Empty your bones of heather and moor,

Your skull of its human matter.

Selkie-boy, selkie-boy, come join your kin,

Eager your kind are to meet you,

As salt sets its seal on your silky skin,

Let green sea rise up to greet you.

Slick is the rock where the waves wash the skerries,
Quick are the birds on the teeth of the reef,
Blue is the water that beckons, that buries,
Dark are the depths beyond your belief.

Hear us and hasten, o sweet selkie-boy,
High are our voices lifted in song,
Offering welcome, keening our joy,
Drawing you down to where you belong.

KARINE POLWART

THE SPACE BETWEEN US

Spell Songs is one response amongst thousands to *The Lost Words*, and to the urgent questions and connections it opens up about what we notice, how we live and what we value. It's no more or less important than what a classroom of six-year-olds paints after one of Rob's spells, or what an elderly grandfather suddenly remembers in response to one of Jackie's rich, expansive images. But in the form of music and song it has, we hope, a certain capacity for flight.

As a writer or maker, relinquishing control over how your work lands and what it means to others, is one of the most liberating aspects of creating. What you make exists then in the space between giver and receiver, where the connections and stories and energies it unleashes are unknowable in advance, and all the more wondrous for that. But you have to leave that space. Music is all about space, how we occupy it with sound, when we let silence be.

The musicians on this album are creatures of many landscapes: moors and machair, market towns and industrial belts, treeless islands and tropical savannah. We've honed our skills knee to knee from master musicians in a long ancestral line, over pints in the backrooms of bars, in school classrooms and conservatoires, and hunched over our pedal boards and laptops. It's a diverse ecosystem.

Some of us have greater facility with shaping words than others. Still others are deft makers of soundscapes, rhythmic wizards, conjurors of melody. In music, there are so many different ways to embody meaning and make connection. And part of the joy of crafting collaboratively in the moment is a sort of dancing into spaces where you can offer something that someone else can't. Equally it takes a willingness to step aside when someone already occupies that space. To offer less than you could requires generosity, confidence, and a commitment to something greater than your own self.

In its wild journeying, *The Lost Words* has become symbolic of this commitment to something greater, to coexisting with non-human life, noticing it, and cherishing it, rather than having dominion over it. It's been an incredible resource and spark for all of us musicians, and writers, in the space it opens up and allows us. We're grateful for Rob and Jackie's explicit permission that we forage within its world in our own ways. Sometimes we've lifted words directly from the page into musical form, or heard a melody embedded in an image. We've fished for riffs and hooks and mantras in Rob's spells, and transformed verse into chorus. We've brought our own unique languages to bear. And elsewhere, we've pared and whittled and shape-shifted what they gifted to us.

The skills and qualities required to make music are subject to the same atomising forces of disconnection and devaluation that catalysed *The Lost Words*. They need our attention, love and advocacy as much as wrens and larks and otters do. To make music is to listen, in the noise of the world, to tune in to the sound of others, as well as to understand and develop your own voice. Technical musical craft requires discipline, diligence, patience, and practice. It's hard work. It's nurtured by elders, teachers and mentors, whether in person or on vinyl, and yet grows new wings from one generation to the next. The spell songs we offer here are born from improvisation and collaboration, from ancient forms and contemporary composition, from empathy and imagination. These are the survival skills of our time. And they're in all of us.

Each musician and maker in *Spell Songs* has their own voice, and space, within the whole, and yet we've become a band, a collective entity, in the mere 8 days during which this music came to be. It's been a joy and a privilege, and a bit of a marvel to all of us.

Song is ultimately for sharing. And it has purpose: dancing, working, lulling, seducing, protesting, celebrating, thanking and grieving. We need songs for it all in the times that are unfolding.

As humans, we take up a lot of space, too much. We need to work out how to take up less, how to leave more. This is not only a job for technicians and politicians. It's a job for musicians, writers and artists too, indeed, for all of us. Whatever comes next, as it must, if we're to survive and thrive alongside the rest of life, will be imagined first, and created next. Together.

We hope you connect with what we've made and pass it on. Do your own work. Write your own songs. Listen out for what's coming.

Now, let the songs fly away!

Go well.

THANK YOU

A special and resounding thank you to Kerry Andrew, Kris Drever, Julie Fowlis, Seckou Keita, Jim Molyneux, Rachel Newton, Karine Polwart, Beth Porter, Jackie Morris and Robert Macfarlane.

A huge thank you to all of those people whose support, enthusiasm and astonishing skills generously nurtured *Spell Songs* into being: Simon Prosser, Hermione Thompson (Hamish Hamilton); Jessica Woollard and Penelope Killick (David Higham Associates); Anna Ridley (Penguin General); Andy Bell (Hudson Records); Alison O'Toole (Designer); Tom Freer (Potent Pixels); Ben Davis (Ben/Dave); Elly Lucas (Photography); Tom Bentley; Joe Jones; Beth Rees and Emma Dexter (JSL Productions); Robin Stenham (Legend); Jo Frost (Songlines); Harriet Simms and Sally Reeves (Glass Ceiling PR); John Garrad (Akcent Media); Chris Watson; Lee Butler; Pete Sharman; Jeronime Palmer (Greta Hall); Anna Pearson-Gregory (Monnington House); Lisa Ward (Rockfield Studios); David Weir (Folk Radio UK); Eva John; Rob Amey; Liz Knight; Lily Macfarlane; Hilary and Bernard Smallwood; Jennie Nichol; Sam and Ted Slough; Molly Please; Thea Wong; Rachel Wood; Jude Holland; Ruth Hardie (Southbank Centre); Bea Colley (Southbank Centre); Dan Whitfield (Aldeburgh Music); Chris Proctor (Town Hall Symphony Hall); Mark Whyles; Dilwyn and Tamsin Davies; Tom Rose; Peter Florence; Heather Salisbury; Mark Anstey; Serena Cross; Tamsin Abbott; Janet Hague; Jacks Guinness; Maxine Shawcross; Sarah Blenkinsop; and Carrie Fitton.

Caroline, Adam and Neil

Folk by the Oak
Quercus Records

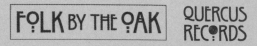

First published 2019
First pressed 2019
002

Catalogue number QRCD004

ISBN 978-1-5272-3961-6

Spell Songs is a musical companion piece to
The Lost Words: A Spell Book by Robert Macfarlane and Jackie Morris © 2017
Published by Hamish Hamilton, an imprint of Penguin Books.
Acorn spell, *Conker* spell, *Kingfisher* spell and the painted wren
reproduced by kind permission of Penguin Random House.

The Lost Words: New text and illustrations created in part
for *Spell Songs* by Robert Macfarlane and Jackie Morris
Text © 2019 Robert Macfarlane
Illustrations © 2019 Jackie Morris

Designed by Alison O'Toole

Photographs courtesy of Elly Lucas
Photograph on page 69 courtesy of Mike Ainscoe